The revolutionary eating guide for a
younger, healthier, longer life

super
foods
for women

BY DOLORES RICCIO

Pages 9–95 © 1996 Dolores Riccio
All other material © 1997 *Woman's Journal*.

This book is an extract from *Superfoods for Women*
by Dolores Riccio (ISBN 1-85479-659-3),
published by Michael O'Mara Limited, 9 Lion Yard,
Tremadoc Road, London SW4 7NQ.

This extract from *Superfoods for Women* is not intended to offer
medical advice. As with any change in your
diet, we would strongly advise consulting your GP first.
Woman's Journal cannot accept any responsibility for
the contents of this book.

This edition has been published by
Geddes and Grosset Ltd,
David Dale House, New Lanark,
ML11 9DJ for *Woman's Journal*,
IPC Magazines Ltd, King's Reach Tower,
Stamford Street, London SE1 9LS.

Printed and bound in the UK.

CONTENTS

INTRODUCTION

YOUR ESSENTIAL EATING GUIDE FOR YOUNGER LOOKS AND A HEALTHIER LIFE

We have all heard about the importance of a healthy diet—it is hard to pick up a newspaper or a magazine without reading about a food that helps to prevent cancer or a vitamin that will give you more vitality.

However, incorporating this advice into a satisfying diet suitable for a busy lifestyle is not easy. After all, who wants to sit down to a plate of raw foods or spend ages preparing a complicated, if nutritious, meal when it is so much easier to reach for convenience food at the end of a hard day?

And anyway, we hear you ask, how much of this advice really applies to us? In fact, women have specific nutritional needs, if they are to remain healthy throughout life. Periods, pregnancy and menopause all require a careful balance of nutrients to prevent illness and promote vitality.

Now, at last, a new book, *Superfoods for Women* by Dolores Riccio (£19.99, Michael O'Mara, ISBN 1-85479-659-3) can help you through the dietary maze, enabling you to *really* enjoy foods which can help to prevent diseases such as osteoporosis, enhance health and slow down the ageing process.

Yes, that's right, *slow down the ageing process*. You can look *and* feel good without having to spend hours in the kitchen or a fortune in the supermarket, leaving you with the time to enjoy your increased health and vitality and more youthful looks to the full.

If you don't believe us, read on. In our book, an extract from *Superfoods for Women*, you will find a clear and concise explanation of the latest scientific theories on how ageing occurs and how we can help to slow it down through a combination of fresh and delicious superfoods. You may have heard of many of the nutrients that scientists believe arrest ageing. But which foods contain them, how much do you need each day and what benefits will they have for you? Our easy-to-read lists will tell you at a glance.

You will also discover just how these foods can be used in the delicious and simple-to-prepare recipes included in the menu section. There's everything from a relaxed soup supper to an elegant dinner of lobster and exotic fruit, to a traditional Sunday dinner of roast chicken and trifle (and many of the recipes take less than 30 minutes from start to finish).

SPECIAL SUPERFOODS FOR WOMEN DISCOUNT

If this extract whets your appetite for more information, why not take advantage of our special discount on a copy of *Superfoods for Women*? Dolores Riccio's indispensable book tells you all you need to know about foods for super energy, whole grains and B vitamins to boost your nervous system, super nutrients to help fight cancer, heart disease, diabetes and infections, and much, much more (including over 200 recipes).

You'll find our discount offer in the March 1997 issue of *Woman's Journal*, to which this book is attached.

SUPERFOODS FOR YOUTHFUL LOOKS AND A HEALTHIER LIFE

SUPERFOODS FOR YOUTHFUL LOOKS AND A HEALTHIER LIFE

Slowing down the Ageing Process
Revving up Our Defence Against Diseases

Why we age and eventually die is a question that has occupied scientific inquiry throughout the ages. Theories about ageing and remedies for this seemingly inevitable process have been proposed since before the pyramids were built (which were designed to protect the immortality of the pharaohs).

We must be doing something right, since our life expectancy has risen from an average 45 years in 1900 to an average 75 years today. Those of us who live to be oldest may celebrate 110 years, but that seems to be our limit. So far. Fortunately, science is never satisfied with the status quo.

FREE RADICALS CITED AS THE CULPRITS IN AGEING

A current theory receiving a great deal of attention is that many of the disabling or unlovely aspects of ageing are caused by unstable oxygen molecules - called *free radicals* - cruising around our bodies. Highly reactive, a free radical carries an unpaired electron and seeks out another molecule with which to combine. And there's no avoiding them! These roving marauders are an inescapable by-product of the cellular process that uses the oxygen we breathe for energy - and about as welcome as rust on your car, another by-product of contact with oxygen. Free radicals are spewed out constantly by every cell in the body as a natural part of the living process.

But we wouldn't want to rid ourselves of them entirely, because free radicals are essential for many of our vital metabolic processes. Even the immune system depends on free radicals to help kill invaders. But like free-roving mercenaries, when not productively employed, they're liable to cause mayhem wherever they lodge. If they happen to bed down in DNA, for instance, they can cause damaging chain reactions - the kind that lead to cancer.

The body has mechanisms for controlling free radicals, but as we get older or are exposed to too much stress or too many external irritants (such as polluted air, cigarette smoke, radiation and X-rays), more free radicals are able to escape the body's safeguards. Free radicals on the rampage have been blamed for everything from the unattractive sags and bags of advancing years to the degenerative diseases that crop up along the way: osteoporosis, cancer, heart disease, Parkinson's disease and cataracts.

ANTIOXIDANTS DEFEND AGAINST THE RAVAGES OF TIME

Fortunately, current research suggests that we have some powerful nutritional defenses - called *antioxidants*, meaning 'against oxidation' - to help protect us from the unwanted actions of free radicals. Sponging up or neutralising free radicals, breaking up their chain reaction and rendering them harmless, antioxidants are associated with lowering DNA damage preventing malignant transformation and other cell ravages, and lowering the incidence of degenerative diseases.

KEEPING MOBILE WITH ADVANCING YEARS

Mobility is an important factor to the quality of life, but, with age, rampant free radicals cause a reduction of muscle mass and the ability to exercise without undue muscle strain. Antioxidant vitamins C and E and selenium have been shown to reduce oxidative harm sufficiently to delay the onset of this 'old age' slow down.

FROM BROWN SPOTS TO SENILITY . . .

Another unwanted free-radical effect is the production of lipo-fuscin, a brown pigment that's been related to senility as well as to those dark patches on the hands and face sometimes known as 'liver spots'. Research shows that antioxidants may offer some protection from these effects of ageing.

SHIELDING WOMEN AGAINST CANCER TUMOURS AND ULCERS

A diet rich in antioxidants will feature generous amounts of fruits, vegetables and whole grains. Endometrial cancer has been shown to be inversely associated with a diet high in fruits, yellow and green vegetables, whole-grain bread, pasta and low-fat dairy products - that is, those who eat plenty of these good foods are less at risk.

In a Hungarian study, natural antioxidants, vitamins A, C and E, demonstrated a protective effect in the treatment of gastroduodenal ulcers. Another study, conducted in China, found that those who took a powerful antioxidant combination were less at risk from stomach cancer.

Vitamins C and E and foods rich in those vitamins consumed by mothers while pregnant appear to protect young children from brain tumours during their early years.

GETTING ENOUGH OF THIS NUTRIENT GROUP THROUGH DIET IS VITAL

Organisations like the National Cancer Institute in the United States and the US Department of Agriculture (USDA) have been advocating the wholefood route to antioxidant defence. Although it would seem a basic good-health move to eat fruit and vegetables every day, a recent population study revealed that 45 per cent of the people interviewed had consumed no fruit or fruit juice on that day and 22 per cent no vegetables. As for the recommended five to nine servings of fruit and vegetables a day, only 9 per cent were actually following that guideline.

It takes three carefully balanced meals a day to fulfil even the basic recommendations. Sometimes it may seem easier just to pop a few vitamin pills, but supplements cannot substitute for a well-rounded diet. They are just what the name implies – a way to *supplement* when more is needed than can be derived from food. We women ought to pay close attention to our antioxidant intake (plus calcium, folic acid and iron, as well). *Good food first* . . . and then, whether a diet needs additional fortification with supplements is an individual decision, which should be arrived at with the help of medical advice.

THE ANTIOXIDANT FAMILY

Because of the press interest this family of nutrients has generated, the term *antioxidants* is now basking in the public's attention. Manufacturers of multivitamin tablets are emblazoning 'antioxidants' and/or 'beta-carotene' on their packaging; some are colouring their pills an attractive shade of pale orange to emphasize the carotenoids subliminally. But if you turn the box over and read the small print for content, you'll find a list of some old friends who've been around for a while but who are finally getting the research respect they deserve.

Some of those familiar names follow. If they've always been a big part of your diet, you probably look young for your age have a good resistance to illness, and can look forward to living several years longer than those who are subsisting on processed and fast foods. But if you're just getting into the swing of the antioxidant defence, you'll find, later in this book, supermeal menus to inspire you further. Because enjoying a diet that offers abundant antioxidants—to protect you from disease and to keep you looking younger longer— is not only easily possible but is the delicious trend of the future.

VITAMIN C, FOR THE INNER AND OUTER YOU

Strengthening the blood vessels, forming and maintaining collagen to bind cells together, healing wounds and helping to resist infection are some of the primary functions for which vitamin C is best known.

The Collagen Connection

The term *collagen* should ring a bell for women; it's often part of the blurb for anti-ageing skin creams. Collagen is a protein fibre, that keeps skin strong and flexible; when collagen fibres begin to break down, as they do after the age of 25, the skin holds less water, becomes dry and allows gravity to have its way. Nutrient creams layered on the skin will not prevent this from happening; treating the whole body to good nutrition is the best defence against the ageing of various parts, including the skin. So, besides all the great things it does for you on the inside, vitamin C is vital to an attractive skin and healthy gums. In fact, the very signs of a vitamin C deficiency are dry, rough skin, bleeding gums and easy bruising.

The Ideal Companion Nutrient

As a helpful companion, vitamin C (aka ascorbic acid) boosts and enhances the power of other vitamins and minerals. It aids in the absorption of iron, and when included in the same meal, it even reverses the effects of inhibiting substances such as tea. Calcium, too, is absorbed better from foods when vitamin C accompanies the meal. Vitamin C is also interrelated with the performance of the B vitamins. A deficiency in vitamin C has been suspected to cause some anaemias by impairing the metabolism of folic acid (a B vitamin vital to women of childbearing age). Vitamin C even assists vitamin E, another antioxidant, to work better at sparring with free radicals.

Vitamin C Helps Women Avoid Heart Disease

Scientists may not have figured out how vitamin C works to protect the heart, but they have noted that people who have a high intake of vitamin C also have a reduced risk of death from cardiovascular disease. Some researchers suggest that increasing vitamin C consumption has a good effect on total cholesterol. In a study by the US National Center for Health Statistics, women in the highest vitamin C intake group (300 milligrammes daily - the present recommended daily allowance (RDA) is 60 milligrammes or 40 milligrammes in

Great Britain) were 25 per cent less likely to die of heart disease or a stroke.

Getting Enough Vitamin C Is Easy

It's not all that difficult or fattening to eat your way to 300 milligrammes of vitamin C. If in one day you consume, say, an average serving each of orange juice, broccoli, peppers, tomatoes and cantaloupe melon, that would put you way over the top. It would also constitute the five daily servings of fruits and vegetables that is currently being recommended. Vitamin C supplements are among the most popular of supplements, often consumed in megadoses. Many people swear that extra vitamin C protects them against the common cold in winter.

Notably, Nobel Prize winner Linus Pauling claimed for years that vitamin C in megadoses helps prevent not only the cold but also cancer. Independent research has not confirmed Pauling's claims, but there are glimpses here and there, such as the Iowa Women's Study in the United States in which high intakes of vitamin C-rich fruit and vegetables were associated with a lower risk of lung cancer - and in other studies, vitamin C has been shown to inhibit cancer cell metabolism and proliferation. In combination with vitamin E, vitamin C was found to protect against air pollution.

Smoking uses up one's supply of vitamin C at a fearful rate, however - so a combination of quitting smoking and getting plenty of vitamin C, as well as beta-carotene and vitamin E, would be an even better lifestyle protection for the lungs. Sometimes women tend to think of lung cancer as a 'man's disease', but in fact, more women die of lung cancer than of breast cancer.

This book, however, is addressing our ability to get most of the vitamins and minerals we need for optimum health through an intelligent, enjoyable diet, rather than through supplements. The good thing about getting nutrients from food rather than megadoses of this or that is that it's exceedingly difficult to overdose. (Some of the side effects of vitamin C megadoses are diarrhoea and/or bladder irritation.)

Strawberries, raspberries and cranberries - besides being rich in vitamin C - also contain a naturally occurring substance called ellagic acid, which doesn't break down when the berries are cooked. Preliminary evidence suggests that ellagic acid may have cancer-prevention properties. It's a pleasure to be able to feel nutritionally correct while enjoying some glorious dessert, such as fresh raspberry pie or poached pears with cranberries.

Perhaps the bottom line here should be that people who maintain a high intake of vitamin C simply live longer than those who do not, according to a study of the dietary habits of 10,000 people in their seventies. Statistically, women gain an extra year, men gain five years. But before you begin to think nature is being unfair to us, remember that women outlive men by seven years anyway.

Superfood Sources of Vitamin C

Asparagus	Kiwi fruit
Berries	Mango and papaya
Broccoli	Melons
Cabbage and Brussels sprouts	Peppers, including hot peppers
Cauliflower	Potatoes, especially sweet potatoes
Citrus fruits	
Kale	Tomatoes

FOR A QUICK BOOST OF VITAMIN C

A glass of orange, grapefruit or cranberry juice

A tangerine (or two, if they're small)

Half a grapefruit

A wedge of cantaloupe or honeydew melon

Raw broccoli and/or cauliflower with a low-fat, calcium rich cheese dip

A snack of cherry tomatoes

A dish of strawberries or raspberries

A side serving of coleslaw with that sandwich for lunch

VITAMIN E AND SELENIUM, A DYNAMIC DUO FOR WOMEN

Like a good marriage, antioxidants vitamin E and selenium have a synergistic relationship. Selenium, an important mineral that's part of the antioxidant package inside the body, brings out the best in vitamin E. Vitamin E has the distinction of being our oldest recognised antioxidant - actually a group of fat-soluble compounds. Because they were discovered to have an important role in animal reproduction, these compounds were named *tocopherols*, from the Greek 'to carry and bear offspring' (but this role has not been shown to carry over to humans).

Owing to a plethora of unconfirmed health claims made for vitamin E in the past, scientists tended to stay away from these muddy waters until rather recently. But new research has confirmed some very real benefits that vitamin E confers.

Strengthening the Immune System Against Cancer

Both substances are immune-system stimulants, working well in tandem. In studies, antibody production was boosted thirtyfold when a combination of vitamin E and selenium was administered.

Vitamin E has been demonstrated to serve as a chain-breaking antioxidant, meaning it protects against runaway chain reactions of free radicals that are implicated in membrane and cellular ageing processes as well as many diseases such as cancer.

Research results are mixed on whether vitamin E foods or supplements lessen the risk of breast cancer. A Chinese study found a combination of vitamins E, A and selenium inhibited breast cancer cells in lab experiments. A US study of postmenopausal women in Boston found the risk of breast cancer was decreased among those who had the highest intake of vitamin E from food, but not from supplements. Vitamin E supplements of 600 milligrammes have been used to treat fibrocystic breast disease with a 70 per cent success rate. But the extensive Harvard Medical School's Nurses' Health Study in the United States found that those taking vitamin E and C supplements were as likely to get breast cancer as those who were not taking the supplements.

Along with beta-carotene, vitamin E may protect against mouth and throat cancer, according to a recent study. Researchers involved in this investigation believe that the combination of vitamin E and beta-carotene has a potential role in chemo-prevention of these malignancies.

Although population studies have shown that there is a relationship between low selenium status and deaths from cancer of the breast, digestive tract, liver and respiratory organs, scientists still feel there is insufficient evidence to support a recommendation for taking selenium supplements as a cancer-preventive method.

Vitamin E Defends Against Heart Disease

Since a number of studies have confirmed that women are less at risk from heart disease if their intake of vitamin E is high, there's every reason to keep up one's intake of this antioxidant while the jury is still out on the breast cancer effect. Preliminary evidence gathered in that same nurses' study has shown that vitamin E supplements are associated with a decreased risk of heart attacks in women. In another study, vitamin E supplements of 500 milligrammes elevated the helpful HDL cholesterol by 14 per cent.

Sun Worshippers Take Note

Of course, we've all learned by now that too much exposure to the sun's rays ages the skin prematurely and puts us in danger of skin cancer. In studies, vitamin E has actually reversed the effects of ultraviolet light radiation on the skin. The application of vitamin E to cuts and skin abrasions to minimise scarring has found some favour with the general public, but research hasn't established these claims as valid.

Lack of Selenium Could Be Implicated in Sudden Infant Death Syndrome

Produce grown locally or animals fed on grains grown where the soil is rich in selenium are the major sources of this trace mineral in the diet. New Zealand, recognising a health problem inherent in its severely selenium-deficient soil, has done considerable research on the effects of selenium deficiency. One extensive survey has implicated the selenium-poor milk of New Zealand cows in sudden infant death syndrome (SID).

Vitamin E's Effect on Menopausal and PMS Symptoms

Nancy Woods, in her *Complete Book of Women's Health*, comments that little attention is given to the problems of menopausal women, 'especially what might have prevented symptoms'. For one of the most distressing symptoms - hot flushes - Dr Woods lists self-help approaches women can try, including vitamin E and ginseng, an Asian herb. She cites a study suggesting that oestrogen replacement therapy, the most commonly prescribed remedy, seems to postpone rather than avert the problem. The hot flushes reappear when one stops taking the hormone.

There have been some very promising results in the use of vitamin E to relieve symptoms of premenstrual syndrome, but it's still early days in this research and the tests need more confirmation. Meanwhile, a diet rich in vitamin E has so many benefits – might as well keep those vitamin E levels up with good food during other stressful times, too.

About Supplements

If you're dosing yourself with supplements, keep in mind that vitamin E is toxic in megadoses, as is selenium. One more instance of, 'if a little is good, it doesn't mean that a lot is better'. Consult your doctor for a recommendation on the amount that's right for you. In the wake of recent promising heart studies, some doctors are prescribing 400 international units (IUs) of vitamin E to their patients.

Recent USDA surveys found that women in the 19 to 50 year age bracket average less than 90 per cent of the RDA for vitamin E (which is only 10 milligrammes in the United States and 3-4 milligrammes in Great Britain) while men consume nearer 100 per cent. But you can increase your intake of vitamin E and selenium just by eating the right foods - and good food is a pleasure in itself!

Superfood Sources of Vitamin E

Asparagus
Fish: mackerel, salmon
Greens, dark leafy
Nuts: almonds, hazelnuts, peanuts
Oils, vegetable
Shellfish: shrimps, scallops, clams
Soya beans
Sunflower seeds
Wheatgerm and whole-grain foods

Superfood Sources of Selenium

Brazil nuts
Fish: swordfish, tuna, flounder
Mushrooms
Shellfish: lobster, oysters, crabmeat, shrimps
Sunflower seeds
Wheatgerm and whole-grain foods

QUICK LUNCH FOODS RICH IN VITAMIN E

Peanut butter on wholemeal toast
Salmon salad on a whole-grain bap
A cup of clam chowder
Chilled asparagus tips with an olive-oil vinaigrette
A snack of whole almonds
A couple of hazelnut biscuits

> ### FAIRLY FAST FOOD FULL OF SELENIUM
>
> A tuna sandwich on rye bread
> A crabmeat salad (the real thing, not imitation)
> Stuffed mushrooms (even better if homemade with
>   wheatgerm in the stuffing!)
> A couple of Brazil nuts (yes, that's plenty for one day -
>   these nuts are especially rich!)
> A snack of sunflower seeds

VITAMIN A AND THE CAROTENOID BONUS

Vitamin A has been a headline grabber for the past two decades, and for good reason - some of the health and beauty claims made for this nutrient border on the downright miraculous. But as population and laboratory studies affirming its wonders continue to be published; we find there's more than 'an ounce of prevention' in vitamin A worth our attention - especially against cancer.

Vitamin A comes to us from nature in two forms: animal and vegetable. The former (technically, *retinol* or *retinyl esters*) found in offal and dairy products, is known as *preformed vitamin A*. It's immediately available for use in the body; it's also a fat-soluble nutrient that is stored in the liver, and too high a dose - such as you might get from supplements, not food - can be quite toxic. The vegetable form, called *provitamin A*, is a precursor substance that your body has to convert to a usable form. Provitamin A includes the carotenoids, found in dark green and orange plant foods, of which beta-carotene is the most widely publicised.

Too much beta-carotene is not considered to be poisonous, except to heavy drinkers, but it might turn your skin yellow—a condition that reverses itself when the overdose is discontinued.

Besides beta-carotene, some lesser known carotenoids working against cancer are: alpha-carotene, notable in carrots; betacryptoxanthin, found in large amounts in oranges and tangerines; lycopene, associated with a red colour, such as in tomatoes and strawberries; plus lutein and zeaxanthin, found in those dark leafy greens.

Vitamin A Wards off Infection

Vitamin A does a multitude of great things for the body. For one, it wards off infection on a day-to-day basis. Taking vitamin A has been shown to boost immunity by increasing antibody activity and speeding up the production of various disease-fighting cells. It's something to keep in mind when the cold and flu season is at hand.

A Vitamin for the Eyes, Skin, Hair, Nails

Definitely the eye vitamin, vitamin A helps to avert night blindness, corneal lesions and cataracts.

It's a beauty vitamin, too. Carotenoid-rich foods are needed to keep skin, hair and nails looking their best. Recently, vitamin A derivatives have been used in several forms to cure acne and psoriasis; and (this was the big beauty news!) Retin A, sometimes called the 'miracle skin restorer', has lessened fine wrinkles and sun-damaged skin in older women. (These treatments must be prescribed by a doctor.) Vitamin A is also needed to maintain bones, teeth, gums and glands.

Preventing Cancer and Birth Defects

Recently, the role of beta-carotene, precursor to vitamin A, in forestalling cancer has taken the limelight. Research results on the beta-carotene-cancer link are so promising that USDA and the National Cancer Institute in the United States, among others, are urging the American public to consume some beta-carotene every day in order to lessen the risk of developing cancer. Beta-carotene has been especially linked with the prevention of lung, mouth and throat cancers, but it also plays a role in protecting against other cancers.

The Nurses' Health Study, evaluating the diets of thousands of women over eight years, found a slightly reduced risk of breast cancer in those who consistently ate foods rich in carotenoids. Modest servings of fruit and vegetables containing beta-carotenes—such as one carrot or a third of a cantaloupe melon or a half-cup of broccoli—seemed to reduce the rate of developing breast cancer by 20 per cent. You might think that most women already ate those amounts, but in this survey, one-fifth of the women didn't. Women who ate great quantities of these same foods did not reduce their risk of breast cancer any further.

Studying the food choices of over a thousand elderly Massachusetts residents, American researchers discovered a significantly lowered risk of mortality from all cancers among those who ate the most green and yellow vegetables. Tretinoin, a derivative of vitamin A, has been used to treat a form of leukaemia with some success, apparently restoring a regulatory mechanism to runaway cancerous cells.

Preliminary studies suggest that women whose diets include beta-carotene and other carotenoids are less at risk of bearing children with birth defects.

The Best Way to Get Enough Vitamin A

Although large amounts of pre-formed vitamin A are found in dairy foods and offal, current nutritional research recommends fruit and vegetable sources because they offer a number of other anti-cancer compounds and beneficial fibre without raising cholesterol.

The new US Department of Agriculture guidelines call for at least two servings of fruit and three of vegetables every day. A medium-size raw fruit, a 6-fluid-(170ml) ounce glass of juice, or 50 grammes vegetable each constitute one serving. Easy enough? With good planning, yes, which we'll get to later in this book.

Superfood Sources of Carotenoids

Apricots	Mango
Broccoli	Papaya
Cabbage, red	Peaches and nectarines
Cantaloupe melon	Pepper, red
Carrots	Potatoes, sweet
Cherries	Pumpkin
Greens: chicory, cress,	Squashes, winter
parsley, spinach, turnip	Tomatoes

Superfood Sources of Pre-formed Vitamin A

Dairy products: skimmed milk, semi-skimmed ricotta
  cheese, low-fat yoghurt

A CAROTENOID SNACK IS A CINCH!

A handful of dried apricots

Fresh cherries

A wedge of cantaloupe melon

Carrot sticks or raw broccoli (with a low-fat cheese dip for extra vitamin A, plus calcium)

A baked sweet potato (about 7 to 9 minutes in a microwave)

From the salad bar: Ignore that iceberg stuff! Choose spinach, cress, chicory, tomatoes, carrots or red cabbage coleslaw

Eat up that parsley garnish!

ZINC ROUNDS OUT THE ANTIOXIDANT PACKAGE

When a potent antioxidant package including zinc as well as vitamins A, C, E and selenium was administered in a recent study to over a thousand older people with age-related diseases such as diabetes, arthritis, vascular disease and hypertension, the combination proved to have promising results in improving the conditions of most patients, encouraging researchers to continue with more controlled clinical trials. Although this is only preliminary evidence, it's an indication that those who want to continue enjoying an active, disease-free life - and that's everyone - ought to enrich their diets with the antioxidant helpers, including zinc.

Zinc Fortifies the Immune System

Established as a protector of the immune system, zinc is an important disease fighter. Effects of ageing that result from immune impairment can be partly repaired by zinc. Studies show that even children whose immune systems have been challenged by protein-calorie malnutrition can be helped simply by being given zinc supplements.

Known to accelerate wound healing, zinc supplements are often given to patients after surgery.

Want to Get Pregnant? Feed Zinc to Your Partner!

A woman who is trying to get pregnant would do well to feed zinc-rich foods to her partner. Some cases of infertility in men have been traced to a zinc deficiency. A new USDA study has found a man's semen volume decreased by as much as 30 per cent when he's restricted to a zinc-deficient diet.

Zinc Needed for Good Deliveries and Healthy Babies

Studies have tied low zinc levels in women to abnormal deliveries, nervous-system malfunctions and low-birth-weight babies. On the other hand, taking self-prescribed zinc supplements poses serious dangers for a woman of childbearing years. Stillbirths and birth defects have been traced to taking megadoses of zinc in the third trimester of pregnancy. Unless supplements are prescribed by a doctor, a safer route is to fulfil your RDA for zinc with zinc rich foods. USDA surveys find that men in the 19 to 50 year age bracket average about 95 per cent of their RDA for zinc. Many women, however, are getting less than 70 per cent of their RDA.

Zinc Deficiency May Figure in Depression

There may be some link between depression and zinc levels, as indicated by a recent study comparing these levels in depressed patients. Values were significantly higher in patients who recovered than in those who remained depressed.

Bon Appétit . . . with Zinc

Zinc may be the gourmet's mineral. It's present in many enzymes that are essential to digestion and metabolism. The alteration of taste and smell can be an early sign of zinc deficiency, and zinc is essential to the growth and differentiation of taste buds, an important note for those of us who enjoy the subtleties of cooking . . . and eating.

Superfood Sources of Zinc

Dairy products: skimmed milk, semi-skimmed ricotta cheese, low-fat yoghurt

Nuts: pecans, pine nuts, Brazil nuts, peanuts

Seeds: pumpkin, squash, sunflower

Shellfish, especially oysters

Turkey, dark meat

Wheatgerm and whole-grain foods

Note: While cocoa isn't exactly a 'health food', it's reassuring to know it does offer the chocolate lover a good supply of zinc. Cocoa is a better choice than chocolate, by the way, because it contains much less fat.

A NO-FUSS HELPING OF ZINC

Sliced turkey (dark meat) on wholemeal bread
A plate of oysters
A scoop of ricotta cheese drizzled with honey and
   sprinkled with toasted pine nuts
A cup of cocoa made with skimmed milk
A handful of mixed fruit and nuts
A cup of fruit-flavoured yoghurt

ANTIOXIDANTS AND THEIR HELPERS AT A GLANCE

NUTRIENT: VITAMIN A

RECOMMENDED DAILY ALLOWANCE (RDA) FOR FEMALES

600mcg
pregnant: under the advice of a doctor

BENEFITS

Helps to keep skin, hair, nails and eyes healthy
Defends against infections
Carotenoids may protect against lung cancer and related cancers

SOURCES

Orange and red-fleshed fruits and vegetables, dark green vegetables

WARNINGS

Provitamin A (carotenoids) is not toxic but too much can turn skin yellow. Megadoses of vitamin A supplements (retinol) can be toxic and can cause birth defects

NUTRIENT: VITAMIN C

RDA FOR FEMALES

40mg
pregnant: under the advice of a doctor

BENEFITS

Builds collagen to bind cells together
Promotes strong blood vessels
Helps to heal wounds

Maintains healthy gums
Enhances other nutrients, especially calcium
Reduces risk of heart disease
Part of an overall cancer-prevention diet
SOURCES
Berries, broccoli, cabbage, citrus fruits, kale, kiwi,
mango, papaya, peppers, tomatoes
WARNINGS
Megadoses can cause diarrhoea, urinary tract irritation
and kidney stones

NUTRIENT: VITAMIN E

RDA FOR FEMALES
3-4mg
pregnant: under the advice of a doctor
BENEFITS
Needed for healthy red blood cells and muscles
Protects against heart disease
Stimulates immune system
May help prevent mouth and throat cancer
Protects against sun damage
May relieve some menopausal symptoms
SOURCES
Asparagus, fish, dark greens, nuts, soya beans,
vegetable oils, wheatgerm, whole grains
WARNINGS
Megadoses can be toxic

NUTRIENT: SELENIUM

RDA FOR FEMALES
No British RDA for selenium
pregnant: under the advice of a doctor

BENEFITS
Works with vitamin E to prevent cell damage and
stimulate the immune system

SOURCES
Brazil nuts, fish, mushrooms, wheatgerm, whole grains

WARNINGS
Megadoses can be toxic

NUTRIENT: ZINC

RDA FOR FEMALES
15mg
pregnant: under the advice of a doctor

BENEFITS
Part of an antioxidant enzyme
Essential to taste, digestion and metabolism
Needed for health of reproductive system

SOURCES
Dairy products, nuts and seeds, oysters and shellfish,
turkey (dark meat), wheatgerm, whole grains

WARNINGS
Megadoses can cause intestinal disturbances, premature
labour, and stillbirths

SUPERMEALS FOR YOUTHFUL LOOKS AND A HEALTHIER LIFE

Supermeals for Youthful Looks and a Healthier Life

Recipes indicated by a • follow the menus.

VEGETARIAN PLEASURES FOR FOUR

Pasta Autunno •
Spinach-Stuffed Mushrooms •
Whole-Grain Focaccia (Italian Flat Bread)
Marbled Pumpkin Bars •

Tomatoes, green peppers, carrots and broccoli in the pasta sauce yield a double-bonus of vitamin C and beta-carotene. There's more beta-carotene in the spinach, and, of course, in those pumpkin bars, with walnuts adding zinc. Wheatgerm in the mushroom stuffing and olive oil in the pasta are good sources of vitamin E, and there's selenium in the mushrooms.

<u>PASTA AUTUNNO</u>

**SUPERFOODS: tomatoes, olive oil, onion, green pepper,
garlic, carrots, broccoli, parsley, pasta**

1/2 pound (240g) ripe tomatoes
60ml olive oil
1 medium onion, chopped
*1 green pepper, seeded and
    chunked*
2 garlic cloves, finely chopped
1/2 teaspoon (2g) salt
*Several pinches of hot red pepper
    flakes, plus more for the table*
1 large carrot, scraped and sliced
1/4 pound (120g) broccoli florets

*1/4 pound (120g) runner beans,
    sliced into 2-inch (5-cm) pieces*
*3/4 pound (360g) penne or ziti
    pasta*
*25g coarsely chopped flat-leaf
    parsley*
125g diced Bel Paese cheese*
*2 tablespoons (30g) grated ricotta
    Romana cheese, plus more for
    the table*

Pour boiling water over the tomatoes and let them stand until
the skins loosen. Slip off the skins; chop the tomatoes.

Heat the oil in a large frying pan. Sauté the onion, green
pepper and garlic until they have softened but not browned.
Add the tomatoes, salt, red pepper flakes and carrot. Cook
over a medium high heat until the tomatoes are reduced to a
sauce consistency, for 10 to 15 minutes.

Add the broccoli and runner beans. Cover and simmer until
the vegetables are just tender, for 5 to 8 minutes.

Meanwhile, cook the penne according to package directions.
Toss the penne and parsley with the vegetable sauce. Stir in
the Bel Paese and Romana cheeses.

Pass additional red pepper flakes and Romana cheese at the
table.

MAKES 4 SERVINGS

* Ricotta salata (not the soft variety) or feta can be substituted.

SPINACH-STUFFED MUSHROOMS

SUPERFOODS: spinach, garlic, mushrooms, wheatgerm

10 ounces (300g) fresh spinach
2 garlic cloves, crushed
12 'stuffing' mushrooms (about 14 ounces or 420g)
3 tablespoons (45g) plain dried breadcrumbs
1 tablespoon (15g) toasted wheatgerm

2 tablespoons (30g) grated Parmesan cheese
1/8 teaspoon (1/2 g) salt
Freshly ground black pepper
Olive oil

Wash the spinach in several lots of water and remove any tough stems. Put the garlic in a large saucepan; add the spinach, and steam it in just the water that clings to the leaves, until wilted, for about 5 minutes. Reserve the garlic.

Drain the spinach, and press out as much moisture as possible. You should have about 75g. Mash the garlic into the spinach, distributing it evenly throughout. (Fingers work best.)

The recipe can be prepared to this point several hours or 1 day ahead. Keep refrigerated.

Preheat the oven to gas mark 5/190°C/375°F.

Wash the mushrooms and remove the stems. (Save the stems for another use, such as soup or an omelette.) Place the cups in an oiled baking dish that will fit them in 1 layer. Mix the spinach and garlic with the breadcrumbs, wheatgerm, cheese, salt and black pepper to taste. Stuff the mushrooms with the mixture, about 1 heaped tablespoon each, mounding the filling up. Drizzle a little olive oil on each.

Bake on the top shelf of the oven for 25 minutes. Serve warm or at room temperature.

MAKES 4 SERVINGS

MARBLED PUMPKIN BARS
SUPERFOODS: pumpkin, molasses, walnuts

65g light cream cheese, softened
2 tablespoons (30g) granulated
  sugar
2 eggs, beaten
75g cooked pumpkin
115g brown sugar
2 tablespoons (30ml) molasses

$^1/_2$ teaspoon (2g) each ground
  ginger and ground cinnamon
$^1/_4$ teaspoon (1g) each ground
  cloves, ground allspice and salt
80ml vegetable oil
120g unbleached plain flour
1 teaspoon (4g) baking powder
50g coarsely chopped walnuts

Grease a 9 x 12-inch (23 x 30-cm) square cake tin. Preheat the oven to gas mark 4/180°C/350°F.

In a food processor or by hand, blend the cream cheese, granulated sugar and 2 tablespoons (30ml) of the egg. Remove and reserve this mixture. (No need to wash the work bowl.)

In the same bowl, blend in the pumpkin, brown sugar, molasses, spices and salt. Blend in the remaining egg and the oil.

If using a processor, add the flour and baking powder to the bowl. Process with on/off turns of the motor until just blended. If mixing by hand, stir until smooth.

By hand, fold the walnuts into the mixture, and spoon it into the prepared tin.

Spoon the cream cheese over the top. Use a chopping knife in a back-and-forth motion through the mixture to make a marble effect. Don't overmix or you'll lose the distinctly different colours.

Bake on the middle shelf of the oven for 35 minutes or until

a skewer inserted in the centre comes out clean.
Cool in the tin on a rack. They may fall a little, as brownies
do. Cut into 12 squares.
MAKES 12 BARS

AN EASY AND HEARTY DINNER FOR SIX

Grilled Veal Chops with Orange-Tomato Sauce •
'Shuffled' Chard and Potatoes •
Carrot Salad with Ginger Vinaigrette •
Raspberry Crumble •
or Fresh Raspberries

*Especially easy if you delegate some of the vegetable prepara-
tion! Top vitamin C sources in this menu are the tomatoes,
oranges, potatoes and raspberries. Carrots are bursting with
beta-carotene, and chard adds even more. Yoghurt is a zinc
food. Grapeseed oil in the salad and almonds in the dessert
are quite high in vitamin E.*

GRILLED VEAL CHOPS
WITH ORANGE-TOMATO SAUCE

SUPERFOODS: tomatoes, yoghurt, oranges

240ml orange juice
120ml dry vermouth, dry white
   wine, or chicken stock
75g peeled, seeded and chopped
   fresh tomatoes
1¹/₂ tablespoons (25g) cornflour
180ml plain low-fat yoghurt
6 basil leaves

3 sprigs flat-leaf parsley, with
   stems cut off
1 scant teaspoon (4g) grated
   orange rind
6 large veal loin chops
3 seedless oranges, peeled and
   sliced
Basil sprigs for garnish

In a small saucepan, combine the orange juice and wine or
stock. Boil until reduced to 240ml. Add the tomatoes and
simmer for 3 minutes; remove from the heat.

Blend the cornflour into the yoghurt. Whisk the yoghurt into the hot orange-tomato sauce; stir constantly over a medium heat until the mixture is thick and bubbling. Simmer for 1 to 2 minutes longer.

Snip the herbs; stir the herbs and grated rind into the sauce and remove it from the heat.

The sauce can be made several hours or 1 day ahead, kept chilled, and reheated when needed. It can also be frozen, thawed and reheated as a quick sauce for almost any grilled meat.

Grill the chops until medium-rare, for about 5 minutes per side. To serve, divide the sauce among 6 warm plates and top each with a chop. Garnish with orange slices and basil sprigs.

MAKES 6 SERVINGS

'SHUFFLED' CHARD AND POTATOES
SUPERFOODS: potatoes, chard, garlic

*Other greens, such as broccoli or spinach, can be easily
substituted.*

2 pounds (960g) boiling potatoes, Salt and freshly ground black
   such as red potatoes   pepper
1 pound (480g) Swiss chard   2 or more tablespoons (30ml)
2 tablespoons (30ml) olive oil   balsamic vinegar
1 large garlic clove, finely
   chopped

Peel the potatoes and cut them into ¼-inch-thick (¾-cm)
half rounds. Boil them in salted water until tender, for about
8 minutes. Drain well.

Wash the chard. Remove any large stems and dice them. Put
the leaves and chopped stems into a large saucepan, and
steam in just the water that clings to the leaves until the
vegetable is tender, for about 3 minutes. Add more water if
necessary. Drain well, pressing out the moisture with the
back of a spoon.

Heat the olive oil in a large frying pan, add the potatoes, and
fry them until they begin to brown. Add the garlic; cook for
1 minute.

Add the greens, and 'shuffle' them together until piping hot
and fragrant.

Season with salt and pepper to taste, and sprinkle with
balsamic vinegar.

MAKES 6 SERVINGS

CARROT SALAD WITH GINGER VINAIGRETTE
SUPERFOODS: carrots, grapeseed oil, garlic, ginger

Grapeseed and walnut oils are great sources of vitamin E - as well as adding their distinctive flavours to salad dressings.

4 medium carrots   1 large cucumber

For the vinaigrette
80ml grapeseed or olive oil $^1/_8$ teaspoon ($^1/_2$ g) each
60ml rice vinegar*   white pepper, salt and
1 tablespoon (15g) finely grated   sugar
  fresh ginger

Scrape and coarsely grate the carrots. (This can be done quickly in a food processor.) Peel and scrape the seeds out of the cucumber; cut it into strips. Combine the vegetables in a shallow salad bowl.

Combine the vinaigrette ingredients in a jar and shake well. Dress the salad with the vinaigrette, and let the mixture stand at room temperature while you prepare the rest of the menu.

MAKES 6 SERVINGS
*If you use seasoned rice vinegar, omit salt and sugar.

<u>RASPBERRY CRUMBLE</u>
SUPERFOODS: raspberries, almonds

*This 'humble crumble' dessert has the same flavour
combination as a sophisticated torte—but can be tossed together
in just a few minutes! You will need a food processor, however,
to prepare the topping.*

400g unsweetened frozen whole
   raspberries, partly thawed
75g sugar

3 tablespoons (45g)
   quick-cooking tapioca

For the topping
50g blanched whole almonds
30g plain flour
3 tablespoons (45g) sugar

2 tablespoons (30g) unsalted
   butter
$1/4$ teaspoon (1ml) almond
   essence*

Preheat the oven to gas mark 5/190°C/375°F.
Combine the raspberries, sugar, and tapioca in a 12-inch
(30-cm) glass baking dish, and stir to blend.
In a food processor, grind the almonds until fine, then blend
in the flour, sugar and butter. Lastly, add the almond
flavouring. The topping should have the texture of rough
breadcrumbs.
Sprinkle the topping evenly over the raspberries, and bake
for 30 to 35 minutes, until bubbly throughout. If the topping gets brown too fast, cover the crumble with a sheet of
foil, not tucked in. Serve warm or at room temperature.
MAKES 6 SERVINGS
*Real, not artificial flavouring. Usually found in health-food
shops.

43

A COMFORTING SOUP SUPPER FOR FOUR

Butternut and Lentil Soup with Chillies •
Tuna and Mixed Green Salad •
Wholemeal Rolls, homemade • or from a bakery
Melon Balls With Fresh Strawberries

Wholemeal flour gives you plenty of vitamin E, selenium and zinc (and many other benefits), and tuna is one of the greatest sources of selenium. The chilli-spiced soup is rich in flavour - and in beta-carotene, thanks to the butternut squash! Dark leafy greens add more, plus vitamin E. Refreshing, low-calorie melon is nonetheless bursting full of vitamin C and beta-carotene.

BUTTERNUT AND
LENTIL SOUP WITH CHILLIES

SUPERFOODS: onion, garlic, lentils, tomato sauce, butternut squash, chillies

You'll probably have the bonus of leftover soup, which can be served on another day, or frozen for later use. Suggestions for reheating are included in the recipe.

2 tablespoons (30ml) olive oil
1 large onion, chopped
1 celery stalk with the leaves, chopped
1 garlic clove, finely chopped
1½ litres chicken stock
100g lentils which do not require pre-soaking, picked over and rinsed

240ml Italian tomato sauce like Passata
400g peeled and diced butternut squash
120g finely chopped mild chilli peppers
1 teaspoon (4g) each dried coriander and ground cumin

In a large saucepan, heat the oil and sauté the onion, celery and garlic until they have softened, for about 5 minutes. Add all the remaining ingredients.

Simmer the soup for about 1 hour, until the lentils are quite tender but the squash still retains its shape, stirring occasionally, more often towards the end of the cooking time. Taste to correct seasoning; you may want some salt, depending on the stock you used.

The soup can be made 1 day ahead. Keep refrigerated. Reheat carefully, because thick soups tend to stick. A microwave takes the worry out of this.

MAKES 2½ QUARTS (3 LITRES)

TUNA AND MIXED GREEN SALAD
SUPERFOODS: tuna, dark leafy salad greens, onion

*I don't use any oil in this salad, because the oil that clings to the
drained tuna seems enough.*

180g tinned tuna in oil
3 tablespoons (45ml) red wine
  vinegar
400g bite-size dark greens:
  choose at least 2 from romaine or
  cos lettuce, tender spinach, chicory

About 50g Sweetened Red
  Onion Rings (see following
  recipe)
Freshly ground black pepper

Drain the tuna. Put it into a salad bowl and flake it slightly.
Sprinkle it with the wine vinegar. Put the greens and drained
red onion rings on top.

*The salad can be made several hours ahead. Don't toss it until
ready to serve. Keep refrigerated.*

When ready to serve, grind some pepper on top, to taste,
and toss the salad well.

MAKES 4 SERVINGS

SWEETENED RED ONION RINGS

Try these onions in a winter salad with sliced oranges!

1 large red onion
1 tablespoon (15g) sugar

120ml red wine vinegar

Peel the onion, slice it, and separate the slices into rings, discarding the small white centre of each ring. In a soup dish, stir the sugar into the vinegar until dissolved. Marinate the onion rings in this mixture for $1/2$ to 1 hour at room temperature, turning often. Drain off and discard the vinegar before using.

The onions can be made up to 2 days in advance. Cover well and keep refrigerated. The longer they marinate, the sweeter they will be.

WHOLEMEAL ROLLS
SUPERFOODS: wholemeal flour

One of the easiest of yeast bread recipes!

10g active dried yeast
2 teaspoons (8g) sugar
240ml very warm water
240g wholemeal flour
240g unbleached plain flour

1 teaspoon (4g) salt
2 tablespoons (30ml) olive oil
1 egg, beaten

Add the yeast and sugar to the water, and allow it to stand for 5 minutes. The yeast should bubble up.

Combine the flours, salt and olive oil in the work bowl of an electric mixer fitted with a dough hook. (Don't substitute a food processor; this dough gets so elastic, it may stop the blades from turning and overheat the motor.) Stir in the yeast mixture. Knead the dough with the dough hook for 5 minutes or until it forms a smooth, elastic ball that springs back when pressed. (Alternatively, combine the ingredients in a large bowl. Knead by hand on a floured board for about 10 minutes.)

Put the dough in an oiled bowl, cover with cling film, and let it rise in a warm place until doubled, for about $1^1/_2$ hours.

Oil a 9 x13-inch (23 x 33-cm) baking tray and sprinkle it with cornmeal such as polenta. Knead the dough briefly, and form it into a rope. Cut the rope into 12 pieces, and form the pieces into plain round rolls. Put them onto the tray in 4 rows of 3 rolls each. Let them rise, covered with a towel, until doubled, for about 1 hour.

Preheat the oven to gas mark 5/190°C/375°F.

Brush the rolls with the egg mixture, and bake them for 25 to 30 minutes, until they are brown and sound hollow when tapped.

Garlic Rolls: Add 1 to 2 finely chopped garlic cloves to the dough. Blend well.

Cheese Rolls: Add 100g coarsely grated Parmesan cheese to the dough. If you substitute the powdery store-grated cheese, use less: 50-70g.

Fennel and Black Pepper Rolls: Add 1 teaspoon (4g) each coarsely grated black pepper and fennel seeds to the dough.
MAKES 12 ROLLS

A SPICY CHICKEN DINNER FOR FOUR

African Chicken Stew •
Brown Basmati Rice •
Salad of Bitter Greens (Chicory, Dandelion, Radicchio)
with Herb Vinaigrette •
Golden Cornmeal-Carrot Cake •
or Sliced Fresh Papaya

Peanuts, a favourite African flavouring, are a great source of zinc. Besides peanut butter, the other stew ingredients—tomatoes and peppers—contribute their share of vitamin C, while dark leafy greens in the salad yield beta-carotene. And so do carrots in the golden cake (or papaya). Rice bran, found in brown rice, scores high in vitamin E.

AFRICAN CHICKEN STEW

SUPERFOODS: green pepper, onions, garlic, tomatoes, peanut butter, brown rice

Although nutritious, peanut butter is high in fat. The rest of this menu is low in fat, but if you're watching those grammes closely, you can reduce the amount of peanut butter by half.

8 skinless chicken thighs	420g tinned tomatoes with juice
3 tablespoons (45ml) vegetable oil	$^1/_2$ teaspoon (2g) salt
100g chopped green pepper	$^1/_4$ teaspoon (1g) black pepper
50g chopped onion	1 dried hot chilli pepper
1 teaspoon (4g) finely chopped garlic	120ml creamy peanut butter
	Hot red pepper flakes

In a 12-inch (30-cm) frying pan (or in 2 batches), brown the chicken pieces in the oil and remove them. Add the green pepper, onion and garlic; sauté until softened but not brown, for about 5 minutes.

Add the tomatoes, salt, black pepper and chilli. Simmer the sauce uncovered for 10 minutes, stirring occasionally and breaking up the tomatoes.

Add the chicken, cover, and cook over a low heat for 20 to 30 minutes, until the chicken is cooked through. Remove the chicken and mix in the peanut butter until smooth.

The stew can be made up to a day ahead. Keep refrigerated. Reheat over a very low flame, stirring often.

Add hot red pepper flakes to taste, and simmer for 3 minutes.

MAKES 4 SERVINGS

BROWN BASMATI RICE

Basmati is a particularly nutty-flavoured rice grown in India and Pakistan. The unrefined brown variety can be bought in health food shops that sell organic foods. It should be looked over (for foreign particles) and rinsed before using.
If you can't find brown basmati, normal brown rice can be substituted (40 minutes cooking time), or use refined basmati (15 to 20 minutes).

2 quarts (2½ litres) of water   1 teaspoon (4g) salt
½ tablespoon (8ml) vegetable   150g brown basmati rice
    oil

Bring the water to the boil, add oil, salt and rice, and stir once. Lower the heat to medium-high and cook until the rice is just tender, for 40 to 45 minutes. Taste is the best test. Drain well.

Alternative steamer method: (Even better, if you have the equipment, producing firmer, more separate grains.) After 30 minutes of boiling, drain the rice and steam it, covered, over an inch (2½ cm) of boiling water for 10 to 15 minutes. Transfer the rice to a bowl and fluff it with a fork. If using the rice for salad, spread it out on a serving dish to cool quickly without clumping.

Brown and wild rice: Substitute 50g wild rice for 50g of the brown basmati or other brown rice. Do not try this with white rice or refined basmati, which cooks too fast for the wild rice.

MAKES ABOUT 400 GRAMMES

HERB VINAIGRETTE

To dress a four-serving salad lightly, try 80ml dressing. Each serving will average about 1 tablespoon (15ml) oil.

60ml rice vinegar
2 tablespoons (30ml) red wine vinegar
1 tablespoon (15ml) Dijon mustard
180ml olive oil
1/2 teaspoon (2g) dried coriander or tarragon
1/2 teaspoon (2g) dried basil or marjoram

1/2 teaspoon (2g) dried dill
1/4 teaspoon (1g) dried thyme leaves
1/4 teaspoon (1g) freshly ground black pepper
1/2 teaspoon (2g) celery salt or table salt*

In a blender or food processor, whisk together the vinegars and mustard. With the motor running, slowly pour the oil through the feed tube until the dressing is thick and emulsified. Stir in the remaining ingredients.

The vinaigrette will keep a month or more stored in a jar in the refrigerator. Bring to room temperature before using.

Caper Vinaigrette: Omit the herbs. Use table salt rather than celery salt. Substitute lemon juice for red wine vinegar. After blending, remove the dressing to a jar and stir in 2 tablespoons (30g) drained capers.

MAKES ABOUT 240 MILLILITRES

*But don't use garlic or onion salt; their acrid flavours overpower the herb essence. If you want garlic flavour, squeeze some garlic into the dressing just before using. If you want onion, add fresh onion to the salad.

GOLDEN CORNMEAL-CARROT CAKE

SUPERFOODS: cornmeal, carrots, yoghurt

*Quite unlike the usual moist dark version, this
carrot cake is light and lemony, with an interesting crunch
of barely cooked carrots.*

150g sifted unbleached plain
  flour
60g cornmeal such as polenta
2 teaspoons (8g) baking powder
$1/_2$ teaspoon (2g) grated nutmeg
$1/_4$ teaspoon (1g) salt
4 eggs
Pinch of cream of tartar
150g granulated sugar

120ml vegetable oil
60ml plain low-fat yoghurt
60ml lemon juice
1 tablespoon (15g) grated
  lemon rind (1 lemon)
150g coarsely grated carrots
  (about 2 medium)
Icing sugar

Preheat the oven to gas mark 4/180°C/350°F. Butter and
flour a 12-inch (30-cm) cake tin with a removable rim.
Sift together the dry ingredients. Separate the eggs.
With an electric mixer, beat the egg whites to a froth, add the
cream of tartar, and continue beating until soft peaks form.
Remove and reserve the egg whites.
Beat the egg yolks until light, gradually adding the sugar.
Beat in the oil, yoghurt, lemon juice and rind.
Remove the egg yolks from the electric mixer, and stir in the
dry ingredients. Fold in about one-fourth of the beaten egg
whites to lighten the mixture, then fold in the rest. Fold in
the carrots.
Spoon the mixture into the prepared tin, and bake the cake
on the middle shelf for 30 to 35 minutes, until a skewer
inserted in the centre comes out dry. If the cake begins to get

too brown, lay a piece of foil across the top during the last few minutes of cooking.

Cool for 5 minutes in the tin on a wire rack before removing the tin's rim. When the cake is cold, sprinkle it liberally with icing sugar through a sieve.

MAKES 12 SERVINGS

A CLASSIC SUMMERTIME MENU FOR FOUR

Fresh Salmon Cakes with Mango •
Peas and Summer Squash with Mint •
Steamed New Potatoes with Garlic •
Sliced Strawberries with
Strawberry Low-Fat Frozen Yoghurt

Salmon is a simply super fish—rich in vitamin E (plus B vitamins and vitamin D)! It's easy to recognise the beta-carotene in mangos, but did you know that peas are another fine source? Vitamin C for this menu is found in the peas, potatoes, mango and especially the strawberries!

FRESH SALMON CAKES WITH MANGO

SUPERFOODS: salmon, mango

This recipe calls for poached salmon, but leftover cooked salmon or tinned salmon could be substituted.

2 fresh salmon fillets (6 to 8 ounces or 180-240g each)
Sprigs of fresh dill
30-120ml dry white wine
200g fresh breadcrumbs*
2 tablespoons (30g) chopped fresh chives
2 teaspoons (8g) chopped fresh dill

1 egg, beaten
Salt and pepper
2 tablespoons (30g) cornmeal such as polenta
About 2 tablespoons (30ml) olive oil
1 ripe mango, peeled and sliced

55

Poach the salmon fillets. *Microwave method*: Place them in a glass dish, lay sprigs of dill over them, and add 2 table-spoons (30ml) of wine. Cover and microwave on medium for about 5 minutes or until the fish begins to flake apart easily. *Stove-top method*: Poach them in a covered frying pan, increasing the wine to 120ml, at a low heat for 8 to 10 minutes. Remove from the heat as soon as the fish flakes apart.

Cool slightly. Discard the skin and bones; chop the fish coarsely. You should have about 200g.

(If substituting cooked or tinned salmon, begin here.)

Mix the salmon, crumbs, chives, dill, egg, salt and pepper.

Form the mixture into 8 balls, 25g each. Lay the balls on a plate, and flatten them into cakes. Sprinkle them with half the cornmeal; turn and sprinkle the rest on the other side. Cover and chill.

The recipe can be prepared to this point several hours in advance. Keep refrigerated.

Coat a large frying pan with 1 tablespoon (15ml) of the oil, and fry the cakes until they are brown on both sides, adding more oil if necessary. Remove the cakes and keep them warm. Lay the mango slices in the pan just long enough to warm them slightly. Divide the cakes and mango slices among 4 plates.

MAKES 4 SERVINGS

*Don't substitute dried crumbs.

PEAS AND SUMMER SQUASH WITH MINT
SUPERFOODS: peas

Fresh mint grows so lustily that the smallest garden or window box or windowsill could be home to a useful mint plant. In fact, if you buy a bunch of mint in the supermarket and keep a few sprigs of it in a vase of water, you may find it sprouting roots and ready for planting in a few days' time.

1 small summer squash, diced
60ml water
1$^1/_2$ tablespoons (25g) butter
One 10-ounce (300g) package tiny frozen peas*

$^1/_8$ teaspoon ($^1/_2$ g) white pepper
$^1/_2$ tablespoon (8g) finely chopped fresh mint, or $^1/_2$ teaspoon dried

Combine the squash, water and butter in a saucepan, and bring it to a simmer. Cover and cook for 5 minutes or until tender. Stir in the remaining ingredients, and bring to the boil. Cover and remove from the heat; let it stand for 5 minutes to finish cooking the peas. (If using fresh peas, cook them with the squash and omit standing time.)

MAKES 4 SERVINGS

* By all means, substitute fresh peas (1$^1/_2$ pounds or 240g before shelling) if you can find good ones.

STEAMED NEW POTATOES WITH GARLIC
SUPERFOODS: potatoes, garlic

If your family is squeamish about garlic, the flavour of steamed garlic is surprisingly mild.

1 1/4 pounds (600g) small new potatoes*

1 tablespoon (15ml) white wine vinegar

1 teaspoon (4g) salt

4 garlic cloves

Freshly ground black pepper

Scrub the potatoes well; cut off any imperfections, but otherwise leave them unpeeled.

Put the potatoes into a steamer over 2 inches (5cm) of water to which you've added the vinegar and salt. Cut the root end off the unpeeled garlic cloves, and add them to the steamer. Steam until the potatoes are tender, for about 15 minutes. Season with freshly ground black pepper.

Serve the steamed garlic as a condiment.

MAKES 4 SERVINGS

*Organic potatoes are preferable, since they will be served in their skins. New potatoes can be large or small: the important thing is that they have thin skins and a firm waxy texture. If all you can find are the large variety cut them into the desired size.

A CHOWDER SUPPER ON THE PATIO
FOR FOUR TO SIX

Corn, Tomato and Oyster Chowder•
Wholemeal French Bread
Asparagus Vinaigrette•
Peach and Almond Cake•
or Fresh Peaches

A combination of zinc, selenium, chromium, copper and riboflavin makes oysters an especially potent seafood. Tomatoes and green peppers in the chowder yield vitamin C, and peaches are yet another delectable beta-carotene food. Asparagus, wholemeal flour and almonds are rich in vitamin E. And as a bonus, there's lots of B vitamins and fibre in the corn.

CORN, TOMATO AND OYSTER CHOWDER

SUPERFOODS: onion, green pepper, tomatoes, potatoes, corn, oysters

This chowder couldn't be easier; the preparation is a cinch, and it cooks in about 30 minutes.

2 tablespoons (30ml) olive oil
1 small onion, chopped
1 green pepper, seeded and diced
200g peeled and chopped fresh
  tomatoes*
480ml water
1 teaspoon (4g) ground coriander
1/2 teaspoon (2g) salt
2 large potatoes, peeled and diced

1/4 teaspoon (1g) black pepper
200g fresh corn kernels cut
  from the cob**
8 ounces (240g) shelled oysters
  and their juice
2 teaspoons (8g) cornflour
120ml cold water
6 leaves fresh basil, shredded

Heat the olive oil in a 4-quart (5-litre) saucepan, and sauté the onion and green pepper until sizzling, for about 2 minutes. Add the tomatoes, water, coriander and salt. Bring to a simmer, and cook with the lid ajar for 10 minutes.

Add the potatoes; simmer until tender, for about 10 minutes.

Add the black pepper and corn; simmer for 5 minutes.

The recipe can be made to this point 1 day ahead. Keep refrigerated.

Add the oysters and their juice; simmer until the edges of the oysters curl, for about 2 minutes.

Stir the cornflour into the cold water until there are no lumps. Pour the mixture into the soup, and cook, stirring constantly, until the soup bubbles and thickens. Simmer for 3 minutes.

Stir in the basil. Taste to correct seasoning. You may want more salt.

Corn and Tomato Chowder: Simply omit the oysters for a vegetarian soup with a really rich flavour.

MAKES ABOUT 2 QUARTS (2$^1/_2$ LITRES)

*Tinned tomatoes can be substituted.

**Much depends on the flavour of fresh corn to give this soup its 'creamy' sweetness.

<u>ASPARAGUS VINAIGRETTE</u>

SUPERFOODS: asparagus, red pepper, onion, olive oil

Besides being a harbinger of spring, asparagus is a powerhouse of vitamins C, E, folic acid, chromium and potassium.

1¹/₂ pounds (720g) asparagus	*60ml olive oil*
1 roasted red pepper	*2 tablespoons (30ml) white*
1 tablespoon (15g) drained	*wine vinegar*
capers	*1 teaspoon (4ml) Dijon*
50g Sweetened Red Onion Rings	*mustard*
(see page 47)	*Freshly ground black pepper*

Wash the asparagus, and cut off the tough stem ends. Lay the asparagus in a large frying pan with ¹/₂ inch (1¹/₄ cm) water in the bottom. Bring the water to the boil, and steam the asparagus, covered, until tender-crisp, for 3 to 5 minutes. Drain and rinse the asparagus in cold water. Cool.

Arrange the asparagus on a serving dish. Dice the red pepper. Sprinkle the red pepper and capers on the asparagus. Lay the drained red onions over the top.

Put the oil, vinegar, mustard and pepper in a jar, and shake well until blended. Pour the dressing evenly over the asparagus. Chill until ready to serve.

The salad can be made several hours ahead. Keep refrigerated.

MAKES 4 TO 6 SERVINGS

PEACH AND ALMOND CAKE
SUPERFOODS: peaches, almonds

The frying pan needed for these cakes is a well-seasoned, 10-inch (25-cm) cast-iron frying pan. If you don't have such a pan, you can substitute a cake tin of the same size and depth. My favourite cast-iron frying pan is over 40 years old; I'd say such a pan is a worthwhile investment.

2 tablespoons (30g) butter or margarine
75g brown sugar
25g slivered almonds
150g sliced peaches, freshly peeled, or tinned and drained
120g unbleached plain flour
1$^1/_2$ teaspoons (6g) baking powder

$^1/_4$ teaspoon (1g) salt
3 eggs
75g granulated sugar
1$^1/_2$ tablespoons (25ml) juice from peaches or orange juice
$^1/_4$ teaspoon (1ml) natural almond essence

Preheat the oven to gas mark 4/180°C/350°F.
Melt the butter in a 10-inch (25-cm) cast-iron frying pan. Remove it from the heat, add the brown sugar, and smooth it into an even layer.
Scatter the almonds over the melted brown sugar, and arrange the peach slices in a Catherine-wheel design on top of the almonds.
Sift the flour with the baking powder and salt.
Beat the eggs until thick and fluffy. Gradually add the granulated sugar, beating until light and spongy. Blend in the flour, peach juice and almond essence. Pour the mixture over the peach slices.

Bake the cake in the middle of the oven for 35 minutes, or until a skewer inserted in the cake comes out dry.

Let the cake stand in the tin on a rack for 10 minutes. Loosen the edges, place a round serving plate face down on top of the tin, and carefully invert the tin and plate together.

Serve warm or at room temperature the same day as made.

MAKES 6 TO 8 SLICES

A HEARTWARMING
CURRIED STEW DINNER FOR FOUR

Pork and Squash Curry on Noodles •
Broccoli with Sautéed Garlic Crumbs •
Mango-Honey Tart •
or Fresh Sliced Mangos

*This menu is absolutely loaded with beta-carotene - in the
butternut squash, the mangos and the broccoli - and the last two
add vitamin C. Peanuts in the stew, plus yoghurt and milk in the
dessert, are high in zinc.*

PORK AND SQUASH CURRY ON NOODLES

SUPERFOODS: butternut squash, red pepper,
onion, garlic, noodles, peanuts

*Put the boneless chops in the freezer for a few minutes
for easy slicing.*

1 medium butternut squash
480ml beef stock
1 tablespoon (15ml) vegetable
    oil, or more
1 to 1¼ pounds (480-600g)
    boneless pork chops, trimmed
    of fat and thinly sliced
1 large red pepper, seeded
    and sliced
1 large onion, sliced

1 garlic clove, finely chopped
1 tablespoon (15g) cornflour
2 teaspoons (8g) curry powder
½ teaspoon (2g) mustard
    powder
⅛ teaspoon (½ g) cayenne
    pepper
½ pound (240g) fresh
    Chinese noodles*
25g unsalted peanuts, lightly
    toasted

Cut slices of squash from the unseeded end, approximately 4 inches (10cm) in diameter and $3/4$ inch (2cm) thick. (Save the rest for another recipe.)

Combine the slices with 360ml of the beef stock in a saucepan, bring to a simmer and cook, covered, until the squash is tender but not mushy, for about 10 minutes. Peel the squash using a fork and sharp chopping knife to handle the hot vegetable. Cut the slices into quarters. Reserve the liquid.

In a 12-inch (30-cm) frying pan, heat the oil and stir-fry the pork until it is lightly browned and cooked through, for 3 to 5 minutes. Remove and reserve the pork.

Add more oil if needed. Stir-fry the red pepper, onion and garlic for 2 minutes. Add the reserved liquid.

Mix the remaining 120ml beef stock with the cornflour and seasonings until there are no lumps. Pour the sauce into the vegetables, and cook, stirring constantly, until the sauce bubbles and thickens, then cook on low for 3 minutes longer. Taste to correct seasoning, adding more curry or cayenne if desired.

Stir in the reserved pork and squash. Remove from the heat. Just before serving, bring the mixture to a simmer, but don't cook it any longer.

Meanwhile, cook the noodles according to package directions. Put them in a large serving bowl, and stir in some of the curry sauce. Top with the pork mixture and sprinkle with the peanuts.

MAKES 4 SERVINGS

*Spaghetti can be substituted.

BROCCOLI WITH SAUTEED GARLIC CRUMBS
SUPERFOODS: broccoli, shallots, wholemeal bread

400g broccoli florets
2 tablespoons (30ml) olive oil
2 garlic cloves, finely chopped

l00g fresh wholemeal
  breadcrumbs (2 slices)
25g grated Parmesan cheese

Parboil the florets in boiling water for 3 minutes or until just tender. Immediately plunge them into ice-cold water to stop the cooking action. Drain well.

Heat the oil in a 12-inch (30-cm) frying pan, and sauté the garlic until softened. Add the crumbs, and stir-fry until golden brown. Add the broccoli and cheese, and stir-fry until the broccoli is heated through.

Leftovers are great as a salad - on a bed of romaine or cos lettuce with Honey-Mustard Dressing (see page 73).

MAKES 4 SERVINGS

<u>MANGO-HONEY TART</u>
SUPERFOODS: yoghurt, skimmed milk, mango

Mango flesh clings to the stone in a devilish way. A chopping knife with a thin serrated blade is most helpful in this task.

240ml plain low-fat yoghurt
240ml whole milk
2 eggs
60ml honey
2 tablespoons (30g) cornflour

¼ teaspoon (1g) ground
   allspice or more as needed
1 large mango, peeled and
   sliced
A baked 8 or 9-inch (20 or
   23-cm) pie shell

In a food processor or bowl, combine the yoghurt, milk, eggs, honey, cornflour and ¼ teaspoon (1g) allspice, and blend the mixture well.

Pour the mixture into a deep saucepan (twice as big as you think you'll need) and bring it to the boil over a medium heat while stirring constantly. When the filling is thick and bubbling, cook for 1 minute longer. Watch out for splatters of hot filling.

Cool the filling to warm. Lay the mango slices in the pie shell to form a wheel. Smooth the filling over them. Sprinkle with a bit more allspice, and chill the tart for several hours until firm.

The tart tastes best when served the same day it's made.

MAKES 6 TO 8 SLICES

A TRADITIONAL SUNDAY DINNER FOR EIGHT

Easy Roast Chicken with Sweet Potatoes •
Spinach and Brown Rice Tian •
Romaine, Fennel and Apple Salad with
Honey-Mustard Dressing •
Raspberry Trifle with Chocolate Meringue •

*Homely roast chicken for Sunday dinner, with sweet potatoes
and plenty of dark leafy greens for beta-carotene, raspberries
for vitamin C, olive oil and brown rice for vitamin E, and (yes!)
cocoa in the meringue for zinc!*
*Suppose you have leftovers? Welcome them as a bonus for
Monday night! Leftover roast chicken, well wrapped in foil,
can also be frozen for later use.*

EASY ROAST CHICKEN
WITH SWEET POTATOES

SUPERFOODS: sweet potatoes

One 6 to 7-pound
  (2³/₄ to 3¹/₄ kg)
  roasting chicken
2 garlic cloves, crushed
Sprig of fresh rosemary*
Sprig of fresh thyme*
1 lemon, sliced

Paprika
Ground thyme
2 chicken stock cubes
4 large sweet potatoes
Salt and pepper

Remove the giblets and internal fat, if any, from the chicken.
Wash the bird in salted water, rinse and drain.
Preheat the oven to gas mark 4/180°C/350°F.
Insert the garlic and fresh herbs inside the chicken. Squeeze
the lemon slices slightly inside the chicken before adding
them to the garlic and herbs.
Rub the outside of the chicken all over with generous
amounts of paprika and thyme. Tie the legs together. If there
was fat inside the chicken, skewer that on top of the breast
with toothpicks.
Put the chicken in a large roasting tin that will also fit the
potatoes. Add 1 inch (2¹/₂ cm) of water and the stock cubes
to the tin. Lay a sheet of foil over the top, but don't tuck it in.
Roast the chicken for 1 hour, basting once at the half-hour
mark. Meanwhile, wash and quarter the sweet potatoes. Salt
and pepper them to taste.
Remove the tin from the oven, and add the unpeeled sweet
potato quarters, cut sides up. Baste the potatoes and chick-
en, and return the tin to the oven to cook for 1 more hour,

basting again at the half-hour mark. When pricked, the thigh juices should run clear, not pink; the potatoes should be tender.

MAKES 8 SERVINGS

*A half-teaspoon of dried herbs can be substituted for either or both.

SPINACH AND BROWN RICE TIAN

SUPERFOODS: brown rice, spinach, garlic, wheatgerm

About 1 1/2 pounds (720g)
  fresh spinach
2 tablespoons (30ml) olive oil
2 garlic cloves, finely chopped
Salt and pepper
250g cooked brown rice

2 tablespoons (30g) seasoned
  breadcrumbs
1 tablespoon (15g)
  wheatgerm
2 tablespoons (30g) grated
  Parmesan cheese
Paprika
60ml chicken stock or water

Wash the spinach in several lots of water. Remove any tough stems. Steam it in just the water that clings to the leaves until it has wilted, for about 3 minutes. Remove the spinach from the heat; drain but *do not press it dry*. Season the spinach with oil, garlic, salt and pepper.

Layer half the spinach in the bottom of an oiled 12-inch (30-cm) glass pie dish or other round baking dish. Make a layer with the brown rice, and top it with the remaining spinach. Sprinkle the tian with breadcrumbs, wheatgerm, cheese and paprika.

The recipe can be prepared to this point up to 1 day ahead. Keep refrigerated.

Preheat the oven to gas mark 4/180°C/350°F.

Drizzle the stock over the tian, and bake on the middle shelf for 30 minutes (5 to 10 minutes longer if cold). Let it stand for 10 minutes before slicing into wedges.

MAKES 8 SERVINGS

HONEY-MUSTARD DRESSING

When preparing a salad ahead of time, pour the dressing into the bottom of the bowl. Stir in any ingredients that might turn brown when exposed to air, such as chopped avocado, fennel, apple, or that might improve by being marinated, such as chopped onions or cabbage. Put the crisp greens on top, but don't toss again until serving time.

60ml rice vinegar
2 tablespoons (30ml) Dijon
  mustard
180ml olive oil

1 tablespoon (15ml) honey
$1/4$ teaspoon (1g) freshly
  ground black pepper

In a blender or food processor, whisk together the vinegar and mustard. With the motor running, slowly pour the oil through the feed tube until the dressing is thick and emulsified. Stir in the remaining ingredients.

The dressing will keep a month or more stored in a jar in the refrigerator. Whisk before using, if necessary.

Poppy Seed Dressing: Stir in 2 teaspoons (8g) poppy seeds into Honey-Mustard Dressing.

MAKES ABOUT 240 MILLILITRES

RASPBERRY TRIFLE
WITH CHOCOLATE MERINGUE
SUPERFOODS: raspberries

24 plain sponge fingers
65g mascarpone or cream
   cheese, softened
60ml apricot preserve, melted

200g fresh or frozen
   unsweetened whole
   raspberries
2 tablespoons (30g) sugar

For the meringue
50g sugar
2 tablespoons (30g)
   unsweetened cocoa

180ml egg whites
1/4 teaspoon (1ml) cream of
   tartar

Line the sides and bottom of a 9-inch (23-cm) glass pie dish with the sponge fingers. Spread the sponge fingers with cheese, and drizzle on the apricot preserve. Add the raspberries in one layer, pressing down slightly, and sprinkle them with 2 tablespoons (30g) sugar. Let the dessert stand at room temperature for 30 minutes or so, until the raspberries lose their juice.

Or the recipe can be made ahead to this point and refrigerated for several hours.

Preheat the oven to gas mark 6/200°C/400°F.

Make the meringue: Sift the sugar and cocoa together through a tea strainer to blend. In a deep bowl, beat the egg whites until frothy, add the cream of tartar, and keep beating until soft peaks form. Gradually add the sugar mixture, beating until the meringue is thick and glossy.

Spread the meringue right to the edges of the trifle dish (which keeps it from shrinking). With a spatula, lift small peaks of meringue here and there for an attractive appearance.

Bake for 7 to 8 minutes on the middle shelf, until browned. It would brown faster on the top shelf, but this method will cook the egg white through.

Cool to room temperature before serving. Cut with a wet knife into wedges.

MAKES 8 SERVINGS

SIMPLY ELEGANT DINNER FOR FOUR

Carrot and Celery Soup with Anise •
Lobster and Conchiglie Salad with Peas •
Wholemeal French Bread
Diced Papaya with Yoghurt Custard Sauce •

*Carrots, of course, are a good source of beta-carotene. Peas add
more - and with papaya are the vitamin C foods in this menu.
But lobster? Yes, for its great selenium content! Yoghurt for zinc,
and wholemeal flour for practically everything: vitamin E,
selenium and zinc.*

CARROT AND CELERY SOUP WITH ANISE
SUPERFOODS: carrots, shallots, skimmed milk

*Because celery and carrots are both naturally high in sodium,
no additional salt should be needed in this soup.
Other sodium-high vegetables are artichokes and many
dark leafy greens, such as kale.*

1 pound (480g) carrots, scraped
480ml beef stock
240ml water
4 large celery stalks
25g finely chopped shallots
2 tablespoons (30ml) olive oil
1 teaspoon (4g) anise seeds

$1^1/_2$ tablespoons (25g)
   cornflour
360ml milk (can be
   skimmed)
Freshly ground black pepper
A few dashes of grated
   nutmeg
Finely chopped celery leaves

Cut the carrots into uniform pieces, and put them into a 3-quart (3½ litre) saucepan with the stock and water. Simmer the carrots until very tender, for about 20 minutes. Reserve the liquid.

Meanwhile, in a medium frying pan, sauté the celery and shallots in the oil over a very low heat for about the same amount of time; the vegetables should be golden but not brown. Two minutes before taking them from the heat, stir in the anise seeds.

In a food processor, puree the carrots, liquid and celery mixture. If necessary, do this in 2 batches; don't fill the work bowl more than half full of hot food or it will bubble over when processed.

The recipe can be made ahead to this point. Keep refrigerated.

Put the soup back into the saucepan, bring it to the boil and simmer. Stir the cornflour into the cold milk until there are no lumps.

Whisk the milk into the soup, stirring constantly until it bubbles and thickens. Simmer for at least 3 minutes. If the soup seems too thick, it can be thinned with milk or stock. Add black pepper and nutmeg to taste. Garnish with finely chopped celery leaves.

MAKES ABOUT 1½ QUARTS (1¾ LITRES)

LOBSTER AND
CONCHIGLIE SALAD WITH PEAS

SUPERFOODS: pasta, peas, lobster, olive oil

100g conchiglie piccole rigate
   pasta or tiny pasta shells
100g frozen peas
150g finely diced cooked lobster
   meat

4 spring onions with some of
   the green tops, chopped
80-120ml Honey-Mustard
   Dressing (see page 73)

Cook the pasta according to package directions. Drain and
rinse with cold water until the pasta is cool to the touch.

Bring the peas to the boil according to package directions,
but immediately remove them from the heat, drain, and
rinse them in cold water.

Combine the pasta, peas, lobster, spring onions and 80ml of
the dressing. Toss well, and refrigerate until ready to serve.
The salad can be made several hours ahead.

Taste to correct dressing; add 2 tablespoons (30ml) more if
needed.

MAKES 4 SERVINGS

YOGHURT CUSTARD SAUCE

This recipe can easily be doubled or tripled, as needed.

120ml plain low-fat yoghurt
2 teaspoons (30g) cornflour
120ml whole milk

40g sugar
1 egg, beaten
1 teaspoon (4ml) vanilla
    essence

In a cup, sprinkle the yoghurt with the cornflour, and stir with a small whisk until very well combined.

In a small saucepan, whisk together the milk, sugar and egg over a low heat until the sugar is dissolved. (Do not boil yet.) Whisk in the yoghurt mixture, and keep whisking over a medium heat until the mixture bubbles and thickens. Cook for about 1 minute longer.

Remove the sauce from the heat and stir in the vanilla.

Can be made 1 day ahead. Keep covered with cling film over the surface of the sauce; refrigerate until needed. Whisk well before using.

MAKES ABOUT 240 MILLILITRES

A MOSTLY MAKE-AHEAD DINNER FOR SIX

Turkey Stew •
Wholemeal and Cranberry Pilaf •
Tomato, Green Bean and Watercress Salad •
Orange Frangipane •
or Clementines and Assorted Nuts

The stew and pilaf can be made a day ahead, the salad and dessert several hours ahead. Versatile turkey is noted for its zinc content. Sweet potatoes in the stew and watercress in the salad add beta-carotene. Wholemeal pilaf, salad oil and almonds (in the frangipane) for vitamin E, tomatoes and oranges for vitamin C. There's no reason why desserts can't add extra nutrition to a meal!

TURKEY STEW

SUPERFOODS: onion, turkey, sweet potato, spinach, cracked wheat, cranberries

Don't be put off by the length of this recipe or the number of ingredients. Essentially an easy dish, like most stews, it can be prepared in stages.

1 medium onion, chopped
2 celery stalks, chopped
1¹/₂ tablespoons (25ml) olive oil
2 skinless turkey thighs
  (2 pounds or 960g total)
1¹/₂ litres water
³/₄ teaspoon (3g) salt, or
  more to taste
Mixture of fresh herbs, such as
  thyme, marjoram and sage*

2 carrots, scraped and sliced
1 large sweet potato, peeled
  and cut into 1-inch
  (2¹/₂-cm) chunks
120ml cold water
3 tablespoons (45g) flour
Pepper
Optional additions: fried
  mushrooms and/or sautéed
  red pepper

In a large saucepan, sauté the onion and celery in the oil until the vegetables sizzle. Add the turkey, water, ³/₄ teaspoon (3g) salt and herbs. Simmer until the turkey is very tender, for about 1 hour. Strain, reserving the liquid.

The recipe can be prepared to this point up to 1 day ahead. Cool the turkey only slightly (20 minutes) before refrigerating. Cool the liquid for longer to preserve refrigerator coldness. When you refrigerate warm foods, put them on the bottom shelf, while keeping perishable items like milk on the top shelf.

You should have approximately 1 litre of liquid. Set 500ml aside for the pilaf, and put 500ml back in the pan. Dice the turkey and add that, along with the carrots and sweet potato. Simmer, covered, until the vegetables are tender, for 10 minutes. If desired, mushrooms and/or red peppers can be added at this point.

Combine 120ml cold water and flour in a jar. Cover tightly and shake well. Strain into the simmering stew, stirring constantly until the gravy thickens. Simmer for 5 minutes to cook the flour. Taste to correct seasoning, adding salt and pepper as needed.

The entire stew can be made 1 day in advance, refrigerated, then reheated. In which case, cook the turkey on the same day, not a day ahead.

Serve the stew with the pilaf on the side.

MAKES 6 SERVINGS

* Pinches of the dried herbs can be substituted.

WHOLEMEAL AND CRANBERRY PILAF

*500ml turkey stock (reserved
from the Turkey Stew)*

*150g cracked wheat
100g fresh or frozen
cranberries*

Microwave method: Combine the stock and cracked wheat ingredients in a 1½-quart (1¾-litre) casserole dish. Microwave on high for 8 minutes or until boiling. Stir in the cranberries, reduce setting to medium, and cook for an additional 10 to 12 minutes, until the cracked wheat is tender enough for your taste.

Stove-top method: Heat the stock to boiling in the top pan of a 2-tier steamer over a direct heat. Gradually add the cracked wheat, whisking. When the mixture is thick and bubbling, place it over simmered water and continue cooking for about 30 minutes, until it tastes done. Stir in the cranberries during the last 10 minutes.

The pilaf can be made 1 day ahead. Keep refrigerated. Because of the gelling properties of turkey stock, this cold pilaf can be sliced before reheating, which looks very nice. Place overlapping slices on a glass pie dish and microwave for 3 to 5 minutes, or bake at gas mark 2/150°C/300°F for 20 minutes, until piping hot.

MAKES 6 SERVINGS

TOMATO, GREEN BEAN AND WATERCRESS SALAD

SUPERFOODS: watercress, olive oil, green beans, tomatoes

If good fresh green beans such as runner beans aren't available, use a 10-ounce (300-g) package of frozen green or runner beans, cooked.

1 bunch watercress
120ml Greek-Style Salad
  Dressing (see following recipe)
200g cooked green beans,
  cut into 2-inch (5-cm)
  pieces

1 large or 2 small ripe
  tomatoes (1/2 pound or
  240g), chopped

Wash the watercress. Discard the lower stems and chop the rest. Pour the dressing into a salad bowl, and stir in the green beans and tomatoes. Put the watercress on top.
The salad can be made several hours ahead. Keep refrigerated.
Toss just before serving.
MAKES 6 SERVINGS

<u>GREEK-STYLE SALAD DRESSING</u>

To get those hard little lemons to yield more juice, soak them in hot tap water for 15 minutes or press and roll them on a work surface before squeezing. Or both.

80ml fresh lemon juice
240ml olive oil
1 teaspoon (4g) dried oregano
$1/2$ teaspoon (2g) salt

$1/4$ teaspoon (1g) freshly
    ground black pepper
2 garlic cloves, crushed

Combine all the ingredients in a large glass jar. Cover the jar tightly, and shake to blend. Let the mixture stand at room temperature for about an hour to develop its flavour. After that, remove the garlic, and refrigerate the dressing until needed.

The dressing keeps 1 week to 10 days.
MAKES 360 MILLILITRES

ORANGE FRANGIPANE

SUPERFOODS: oranges, almonds

*All nuts are nutritious, but almonds are especially high
in vitamin E, as well as some important B vitamins.*

2 to 3 seedless oranges
1 tablespoon (15g) butter or
   margarine
2 egg whites
Pinch of cream of tartar
50g sugar
30g plain flour

$^1/_4$ teaspoon (1g) baking
   powder
25g ground almonds (can be
   done in a food processor)
2 tablespoons (30ml) orange
   juice
$^1/_2$ teaspoon (2ml) natural
   almond essence

Peel the oranges, removing all the white membrane. Cut
them into slices, then dice them. You should have 200g.
Drain them in a sieve reserving the juice. Use the accumu-
lated liquid for the juice needed in the recipe.

Preheat the oven to gas mark 4/180°C/350°F.

While the oven is heating, put the butter into a 9-inch (23-
cm) glass pie or quiche dish and melt it in the oven; don't
let it brown.

Layer the oranges in the melted butter.

Beat the egg whites until they're frothy. Add the cream of tartar and continue beating until soft peaks form. Gradually
beat in the sugar.

Mix the flour and baking powder together. Fold the mixture
into the egg whites. Fold in the ground almonds. Gently
whisk in the juice and almond essence.

Pour the mixture evenly over the oranges, and use a spatula to spread it right to the edge of the dish. Bake the cake in the middle of the oven for 25 to 30 minutes, or until the top is golden and springs back when pressed.

Serve warm or at room temperature. It falls a bit during cooling.

The cake can be prepared several hours ahead but tastes best when eaten the same day it's made.

MAKES 6 SERVINGS

BRUNCH OR LUNCH
FOR FOUR ON A BIG DAY

Sliced Kiwi Fruit and Honeydew Melon with Lime Wedges
Salmon and Potato Frittata •
Carrot-Bran Muffins •

*Rev up for the day with beta-carotene in the honeydew melon
and carrots, vitamin C in the kiwi fruit and potatoes,
vitamin E in salmon and bran.*

SALMON AND POTATO FRITTATA

SUPERFOODS: potatoes, salmon

*Italians are fond of egg dishes and will add almost any leftovers
to a frittata which is why there are so many varieties. If you're
short on cooked potatoes, you could add some peas with
the egg mixture. Frittatas call for flexibility.*

2 tablespoons (30ml) olive oil
200g cooked and sliced potatoes
100g tinned or cooked salmon
4 eggs

2 tablespoons (30ml) water
1/4 teaspoon (1g) dried
   rosemary
Salt and freshly ground
   black pepper

Heat 1$\frac{1}{2}$ tablespoons (25ml) of the oil in a 10-inch (25-cm) frying pan, preferably nonstick. Fry the potatoes, turning often, until most of them are browned on one side, for about 7 minutes.

Pick over the salmon to remove any bones, but don't mash it; keep the flakes large.

Beat the eggs with the water, rosemary, salt and pepper to taste. Pour the egg mixture over the potatoes. Scatter the salmon on top, pressing the flakes into the egg with the back of a spoon.

Cook over a very low heat until the egg has set, lifting the edges from time to time to let the uncooked portion seep underneath. The top of the frittata will still be moist.

To invert, loosen the entire frittata with a spatula. Place a large plate over it, and turn the pan and plate together.

Put the pan back on the heat, add the remaining oil, and slide the frittata back into the pan to brown on the second side, which will take only a minute or two. Cut into quarters and serve immediately.

MAKES 4 SERVINGS

CARROT-BRAN MUFFINS

SUPERFOODS: bran, orange juice, carrots, raisins

180g unbleached plain flour
40g sugar
1 teaspoon (4g) each ground
   cinnamon and bicarbonate
   of soda
$1/_2$ teaspoon (2g) each ground
   ginger, baking powder and
   salt

$1/_4$ teaspoon (1g) ground
   allspice
50g wheat bran*
160ml orange juice
60ml vegetable oil
1 egg
100g finely grated carrots
35g raisins

Grease a 12-cup patty pan, or use cake papers.

Sift together into a large bowl all the dry ingredients except the bran. Stir in the bran.

In a medium bowl, whisk together the orange juice, oil and egg. Grate the carrots (very easy in food processor). Measure the carrots and raisins.

The recipe can be made ahead to this point and kept for several hours or overnight. Refrigerate the liquid ingredients and carrots until needed.

When ready to cook, preheat the oven to gas mark 6/200°C/400°F. Stir the liquid ingredients into the dry until just blended. Fold in the carrots and raisins.

Divide the mixture among the cake papers or patty-pan cups, and bake on the top shelf for about 20 minutes. The muffins are done when they're risen, brown, and a skewer inserted in the centre of a muffin comes out dry.

As soon as they can be handled, remove the muffins from the tin and cool them on a wire rack. Serve slightly warm or at room temperature.

Homemade muffins will keep for 3 to 4 days in a plastic container in the refrigerator—or may be frozen for longer storage.

MAKES 12 MUFFINS

* From health-food shops.

A LAZY SUNDAY BRUNCH FOR FOUR

Grapefruit Sections with Honey and Toasted Pine Nuts
Lazy Sunday Ricotta Quiche •
Apricot-Oatmeal Muffins •

Another brunch - this one with lots of zinc in pine nuts and ricotta (calcium in the low-fat cheese, too!). Get your beta-carotene in apricots, vitamin C in grapefruit, and vitamin E from wholemeal in the muffins.

LAZY SUNDAY RICOTTA QUICHE
SUPERFOODS: ricotta, skimmed milk

Whipped up in a processor or blender, this quiche makes its own crust. What could be easier?

125g semi-skimmed ricotta
120ml milk (can be skimmed)
3 eggs
60g plain flour
$1/2$ teaspoon (2g) baking powder
$1/8$ teaspoon ($1/2$ g) white pepper

Salt*
50g slivered prosciutto (or any ham)
25g coarsely grated Parmesan cheese

Preheat the oven to gas mark 5/190°C/375°F. Generously butter a 9-inch (23-cm) glass pie dish.

In a food processor or blender, blend the ricotta, milk, eggs, flour, baking powder and seasonings. Pour the mixture into the prepared dish.

Scatter the ham on top, and sprinkle with the Parmesan cheese.

Bake on the middle shelf for about 20 minutes, until set at the centre. The quiche will puff up, then fall when removed from the oven. Serve warm or at room temperature.

MAKES 4 TO 6 SERVINGS

*Can be omitted, since the ham and cheese are salty.

APRICOT-OATMEAL MUFFINS
SUPERFOODS: oats, wheatgerm, apricots

Packed with nutrition, two of these muffins make a fine breakfast for those who find the crunch of cold cereal too loud in the morning.

180g unbleached plain flour
1 tablespoon (15g) baking
  powder
1 teaspoon (4g) ground
  cardamom
1/2 teaspoon (2g) salt
100g quick-cooking oats

75g brown sugar (remove
  lumps)
25g wheatgerm
180ml milk
2 eggs
80ml vegetable oil
50g snipped dried apricots

Grease a 12-cup pan, or use cake papers.

Sift together into a large bowl the flour, baking powder, cardamom and salt. Stir in the oats, brown sugar and wheatgerm.

In a medium bowl, whisk together the milk, eggs and oil.

The recipe can be made ahead to this point and kept for several hours or overnight. Refrigerate the liquid ingredients until needed.

When ready to cook, preheat the oven to gas mark 6/200°C/400°F.

Stir the liquid ingredients into the dry until just blended. Fold in the apricots.

Divide the mixture among the 12 cups or cake papers, and bake on the top shelf for 15 to 20 minutes. The muffins are done when they're risen, brown, and a skewer inserted in the centre of a muffin comes out dry.

As soon as they can be handled, remove the muffins from the tin and cool them on a wire rack. Serve slightly warm or at room temperature.

In some homes fresh muffins will disappear in a day, but bear in mind that they'll keep for 3 to 4 days in a plastic container in the refrigerator or freeze them for longer storage.

MAKES 12 MUFFINS